WHAT CAN YOU DO WITH *a* POCKET?

written by
EVE MERRIAM

illustrated by
HARRIET SHERMAN

ALFRED A. KNOPF
NEW YORK

L. C. catalog card number: 63-9112

This is a Borzoi Book, published by Alfred A. Knopf, Inc.

For Doug, Josh, and Margot
E.M.

For my family and L.K.
H.S.

WHAT
CAN YOU
DO WITH
a
POCKET?

What,
oh what,
can you
do with
a pocket?

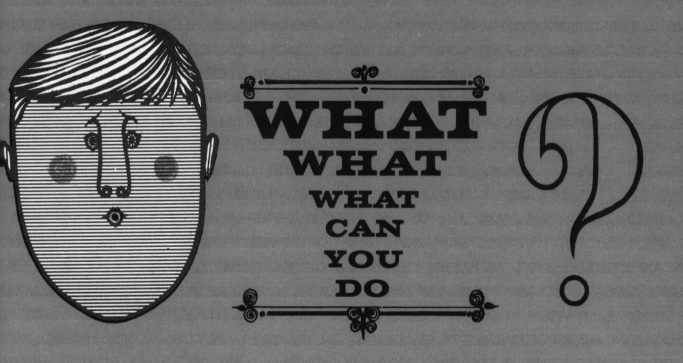

WHAT
WHAT
WHAT
CAN
YOU
DO
?

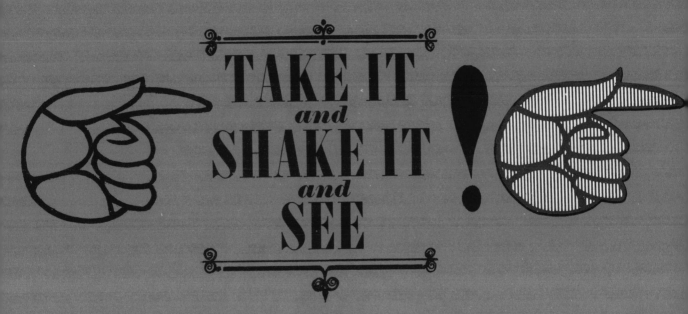

With a

ROPE

in your pocket
you can be a

COWBOY

and round up the cattle.
Wahoo, herd them all home. Yippee!

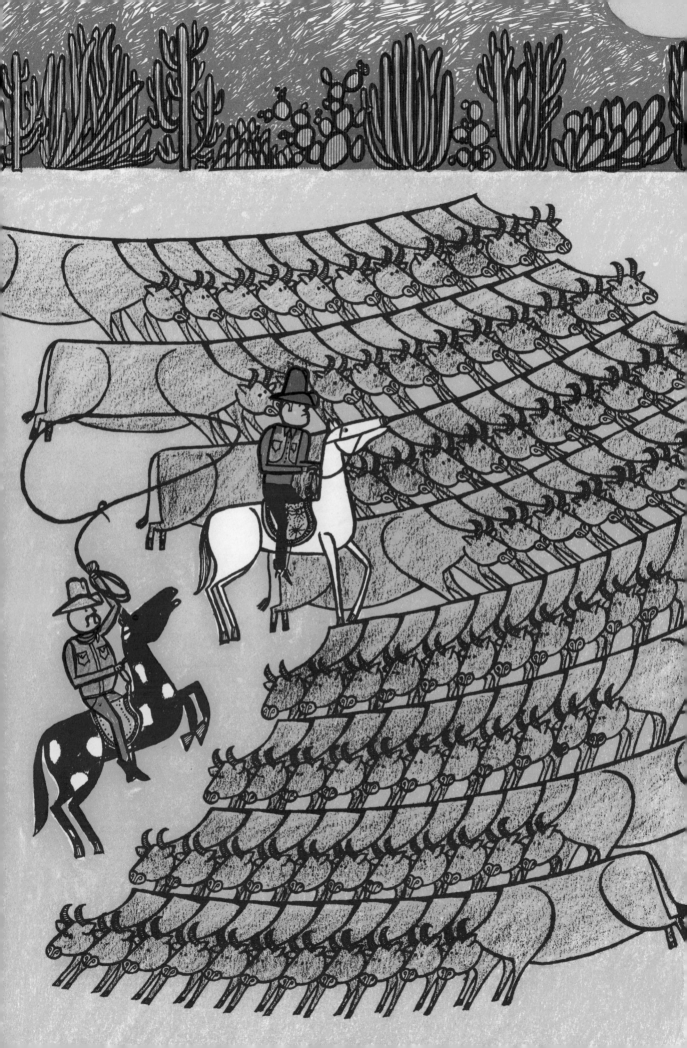

With a
FEATHER

in your pocket
you can be an

INDIAN

Walk tall, Indian brave.
Cook meat by the campfire, Indian maid.
Strap onto my back and sleep tight, little papoose.

With
string

in your pocket
you can have a fishing line.
Heave ho,

fisherman

Tug and pull, pull, pull.
Pull in one big WHALE or a school of speckled trout.

With a

NUT

in your pocket
you can be a

SQUIRREL

Will you crack open the shell and eat the
sweet meat now or save it for the winter?
Scramble up the tree, squirrel.
Run and wave your bushy tail.

With a
WHISTLE

in your pocket you can be a
POLICEMAN

Blow, blow, blow for
the traffic
to

Hold up your hand—
now it has
to

If you have a **BUTTON** in your pocket
you can balance
it on your nose
and be a seal
at the
CIRCUS

Sit up, seal, and flap your flippers!

If you have a piece of

PAPER

you can tear it in half

and then in half

and then in half

and half and half and half

and half and half again
until you have confetti for a

PARADE

Hooray! Here comes the big

PARADE!

If you have a
STICK

you can lead the
ORCHESTRA

Boomlay, boomlay, boom the big drums.
Crash on the cymbals, crash.
Ping, ping, ping the triangle, ping.

With a

in your pocket you can be a

and jingle when you walk.
Oink, oink. Jingle, jingle. Oink!

If you have a piece of cold

you can scare your friends.
Boo! Here's a wriggly worm!

With a
PEBBLE

in your pocket you can do a
TRICK

Make two fists and hide the pebble inside one.
Don't tell me—see if I can guess.
Now, where is the pebble? Left hand or right?

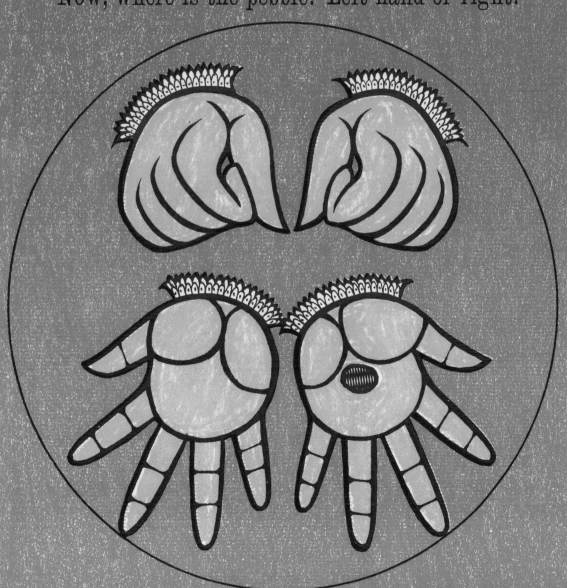

You
can
be a

TEACHER

and
keep **paper clips** and a
pencil
in your pocket.

Attention, class,

1 2 3
X Y Z

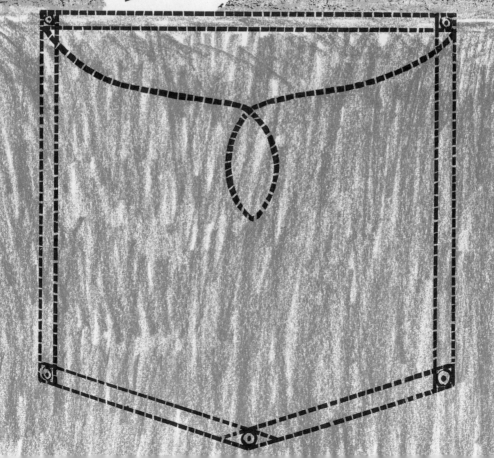

You can write a make-believe *Letter* and mail it in your pocket. Down the chute!

Don't forget to stamp it.

If you have a

HANDKERCHIEF

you can wave it and be a

RAILROAD ENGINEER

Flag the train.
Hoot and holler and toot and call out all the stops.
All aboard for Altoona, Schenectady, Oswego, Duluth,
Chillicothe, Cedar Rapids, Kokomo, and San Francisco!
'Board! All aboard!

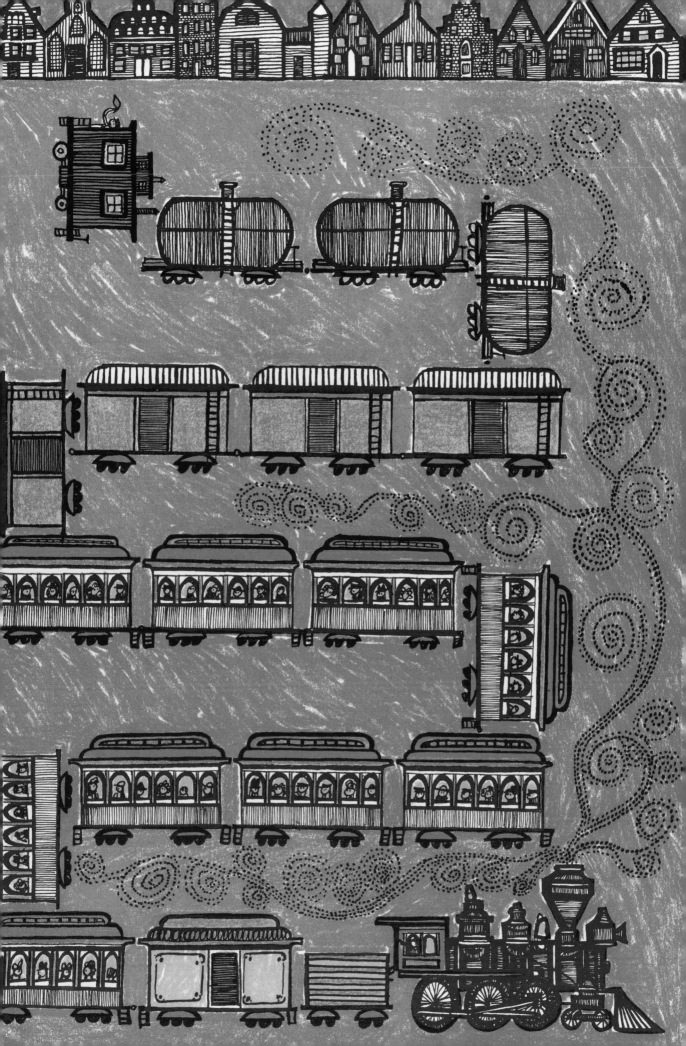

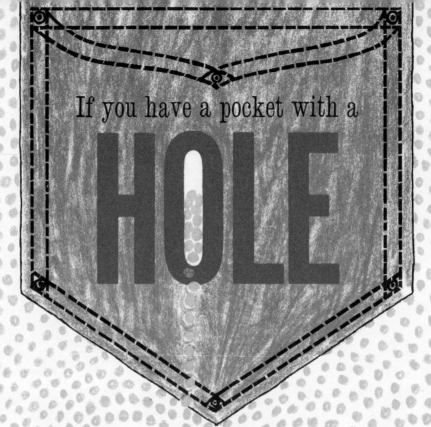

If you have a pocket with a
HOLE

you can
let sand
dribble
through.

Dance
around and
prance around
and dribble it
in a circle.
Or

march and
dribble it
in a square.

Left turn,

right turn,

about face

—halt!

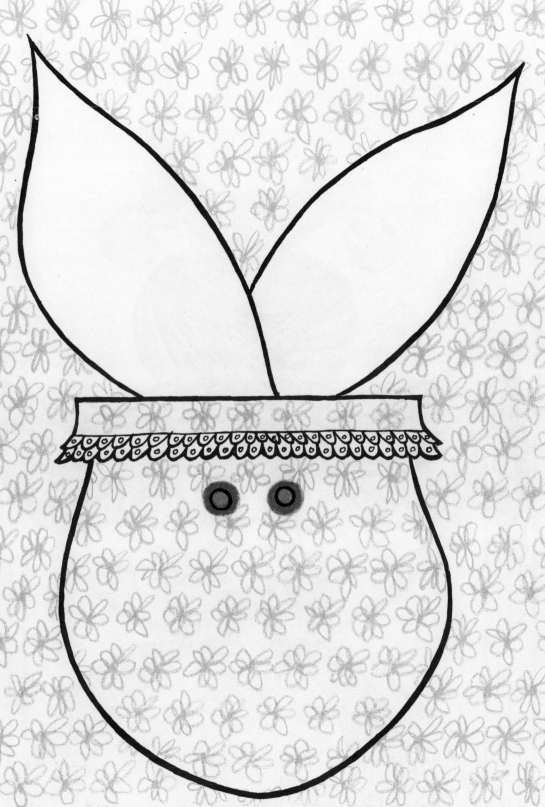

You can turn your pocket inside out
and make it into a rabbit's ear.
Funny bunny!

If you have a *thimble* in your pocket
you can be the
tiniest fairy *Princess* in the world
and put on your thimble crown
or drink ambrosia from your thimble goblet.

Or
you can carry a **SECRET** around with you
and nobody knows what it is
because the secret is in your pocket.
It may be a red rubber band
that can stretch from your nose to your toes.
Let go and zing!

Or a blue piece of chalk to draw the sky on paper.

Or maybe it's a
wish

Dry out a wishbone and
save it in your pocket.

Or a
memory

Remember last summer?
You can keep a warm sea shell
in your pocket to remember it by.

A POCKET IS

your own treasure place.
You can keep whatever you want there,
because it's your own inside house
and everything in it belongs just to you.
A mouse made out of fluffy white cotton.
A little ball made out of crumpled silver paper
that's round as the moon.

A pocket is like the nighttime with the covers all snug tucked in and the stars shining bright above. A pocket can be your dream. What do you want to put in it?

It's up to you.
Put your hand in your pocket,
close your eyes and
dream up a surprise.